MW00886133

Who I Am in Christ

Odessa Coleman

Trilogy Christian Publishers
A Wholly Owned Subsidary of Trinity Broadcasting Network
2442 Michelle Drive
Tustin, CA 92780

Copyright © 2021 by Odessa Coleman

All Scripture quotations, unless otherwise noted, taken from *The Holy Bible, King James Version*. Cambridge Edition: 1769.

Scripture quotations marked MSG are taken from *THE MESSAGE,* copyright (c) 1993, 2002, 2018 by Eugene H. Peterson. Used by permission of NavPress. All rights reserved. Represented by Tyndale House Publishers, Inc.

All rights reserved, including the right to reproduce this book or portions thereof in any form whatsoever.

Cover design by: Cornerstone Creative Solutions

For information, address Trilogy Christian Publishing
Rights Department, 2442 Michelle Drive, Tustin, Ca 92780.
Trilogy Christian Publishing/ TBN and colophon are trademarks of Trinity Broadcasting Network.

For information about special discounts for bulk purchases, please contact Trilogy Christian Publishing.

Manufactured in the United States of America

Trilogy Disclaimer: The views and content expressed in this book are those of the author and may not necessarily reflect the views and doctrine of Trilogy Christian Publishing or the Trinity Broadcasting Network.

10 9 8 7 6 5 4 3 2 1

Library of Congress Cataloging-in-Publication Data is available.

ISBN 978-1-63769-646-0 (Print Book)
ISBN 978-1-63769-647-7 (ebook)

Who I Am in Christ by Odessa Coleman is both brilliant and catchy by using the alphabet to communicate powerful, real-life concepts to children. I can see children growing in literacy and their relationship with Christ!

Pastor Don Coleman, Lead Pastor of East End Fellowship and Former Chairman of Richmond Public Schools Board of Trustees

Who am I? Why am I here? From Genesis to Revelation, the Word of God overflows with His answer, revealing the identity and destiny God gives to His children! This delightful book you are holding in your hands resounds with God's identity and destiny for little ones. As they journey through the alphabet, they journey through the truth of God's Word for their lives. God's children of every age will be blessed, encouraged, and strengthened as they read *Who I Am in Christ.*

Marie C. Teodori, Ed.D. Educational Leadership Consultant

I am not really surprised that Odessa Coleman has written such a profound book for children. She has a love for God and wants to make sure that it's passed on to everyone. Odessa delights in making others happy. *Who I Am in Christ* is a winner.

Karlyn Clevert Smith, CAO, Grace Haven Management, Inc. Retired Educator, Public School System & Retired Banker

Who I Am in Christ is an excitingly delightful way to introduce the characteristics of Jesus Christ into the hearts of young children. It is the kind of book that will delight the heart of a child while simultaneously infusing that heart with the word of God. Expect to hear, "Can you read it again?"

Gwendolyn G. Young, Bishop, Gwendolyn Young Ministries, Inc., Pnuema Healing Academy

Students and families will be blessed by reading the *Who I Am in Christ* children's book by Odessa Coleman. Divine purpose and alphabetic awareness intersect in this book. Young readers will be engaged and treated to beautiful illustrations. The rich vocabulary presents great opportunities for parents, guardians and teachers to expand upon phonics, denotation, godly character and the promises of God. Ms. Coleman does a great job of sharing the gospel, purpose, direction and positive affirmation to young readers.

Jay Jones, Head of School, City School, Austin, TX

In today's society where youth are challenged with peer pressure, it is important that they know their identity. This book, *Who I Am in Christ*, Odessa Coleman, is able to instill into the heart of children a sense of value. The content of this wonderful book will help affirm today's youth with godly character that will enable them to become strong in the Lord, ultimately to fulfill their purpose.

Donna Jones, Educational Consultant, Public & Private School Systems Grades K-12

The content is interesting and applicable to every child, with the added benefit of increasing their chances of finding their personal relationship with Christ.

A thought-provoking message for all children, one that will bring them to a personal relationship with the Savior!

Cynthia D. Poke, Minister of Bethel Outreach International Church, Adjunct Professor of Dance, Johnson C. Smith University, Teacher of Dance, Charlotte Mecklenburg Schools, Master of Science in Health, Physical Education and Dance, Educational Leadership Doctoral Student at Gardner-Webb University

Loved the book!

Who I Am in Christ will inspire young readers as well as adults to learn about their destiny in Christ through the alphabets! It is inspirational, creative, powerful and easy to read! This book is a great book for children of all ages!

Katrina Sims, Family Services Specialist, Resource Family Unit, Richmond Department of Social Services

Who I Am in Christ, by Odessa Coleman, is a thoughtful, unique, and powerful book to teach kids to understand who they are in Christ in a very simple manner using the alphabet. The Bible can be daunting, even for adults, and this book gives children a way to connect scripture to their identity.

Kenneth Mitchell, Assistant Pastor, Mt. Gilead Full Gospel International Ministries

Dedication

I dedicate this book to my son, Daniel Emmanuel, my nephews, nieces, siblings, and mentees.

Acknowledgments

I would like to thank my mother, the late Shirley Mercer-Coleman, a virtuous woman of God, for praying and standing in the gap for my salvation. I would also like to thank my pastor, co-pastor, and assistant pastor for their prayers and Trilogy Christian Publishing for accepting my manuscript. Finally, I thank my Heavenly Father for helping me to write this vision, make it plain, and run with it.

Ask me, ask me, ask me,
who I am

3

If you ask me who I am, I'm

A—Adopted of God

B—Bold as a lion

C—Child of God

A, B, C, and... D—Delivered from the hand of the enemy

E—Equipped to do the work of God

F—Fearfully and wonderfully made

G—Getting my needs met

H—Healed by His stripes

I, J, K, give

me an...

I—Increasing in God

J—Justified

K
—Kept in safety wherever I go

MISSIONS TRIP TO UGANDA

ALGERIA

MALI

LIBYA

NIGERIA

EGYPT

SUDAN

ANGOLA

ETHIOPIA

UGANDA

SOUTH AFRICA

Give me an...

L—Looking unto Jesus

M—More than a conqueror

N–Not moved by what I see

Give me an

O—Overcomer

P—Peacemaker

Q–Quiet and confident in Christ

Give me an R—Righteousness

S—Strong in the Lord

T—Trusting in God

U—Unconditionally loved by Him

Give me a V —Victorious

W—Walking by faith

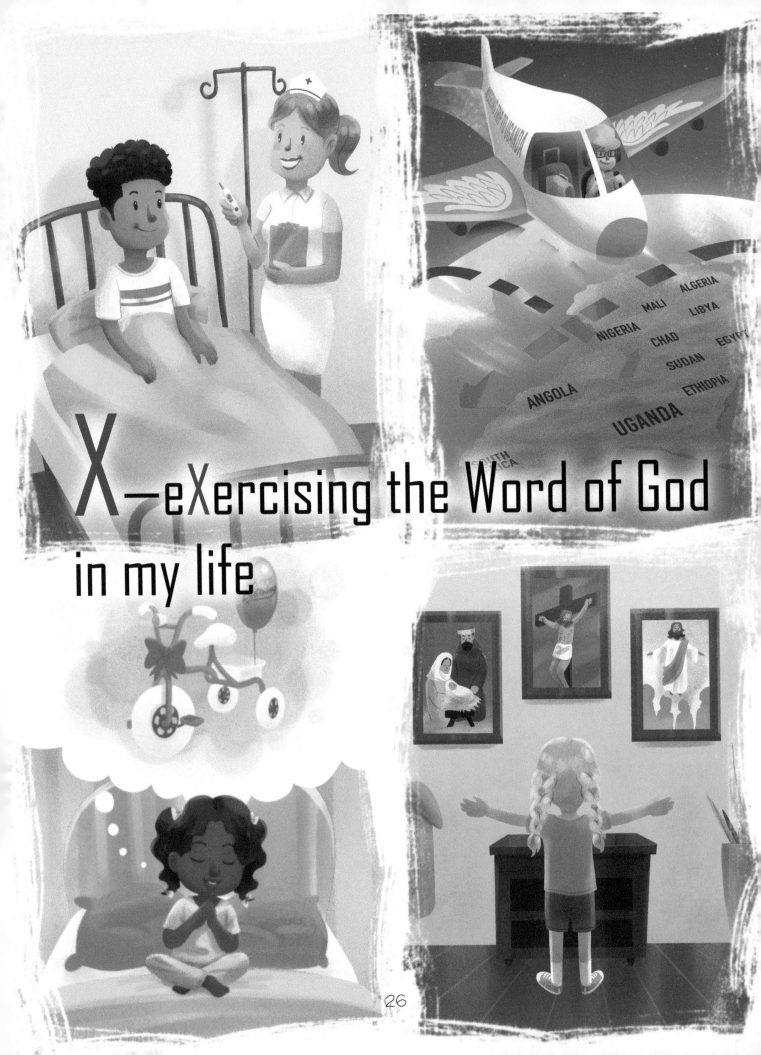

X—eXercising the Word of God in my life

Give me a

Y—Yielding to God

Z—Zealous for the things of God

Ask me, ask me, ask me
who I am

If you ask me who I am, I'm a child of the most high God and loved by Him.

Would you like to become a child of the most high God?

If so, please pray this prayer.

Heavenly Father, I am a sinner. Right now, I ask You to forgive me of my sins. I want to be a child of God. I believe Jesus died on the cross for my sins, and I believe in my heart that God raised Jesus from the dead. Therefore, right now, I invite Jesus into my heart. I confess Him as Lord over my life. Help me, Lord, to develop a personal relationship with You. Help me to read my Bible, pray, and find a Bible-teaching church so that I may fellowship with other believers.

In Jesus' Name,
Amen

Who I Am in Christ

Adopted of God	Romans 8:15/Gal. 4:5
Bold as a lion	Proverbs 28:1
Child of God	Romans 8:16
Delivered from the hand of the enemy	Psalm 107:2
Equipped to do the work of God	II Timothy 3:17 (NKJV)
Fearfully and wonderfully made	Psalm 139:14
Getting my needs met	Phil. 4:19
Healed by His stripes	I Peter 2:24
Increasing in God	Colossians 1:10
Justified	Romans 5:1
Kept in safety wherever I go	Psalm 91
Looking unto Jesus	Hebrews 12:2
More than a conqueror	Romans 8:37
Not moved by what I see	Psalm 16:8
Overcomer	Revelation 12:11
Peacemaker	Matthew 5:9
Quiet and confident in Christ	Isaiah 30:15
Righteousness	II Corinthians 5:21
Strong in the Lord	Ephesians 6:10
Trusting in God	Proverbs 3:5
Unconditionally loved by Him	Isaiah 43:4
Victorious	I Corinthians 15:57
Walking by faith	II Corinthians 5:7

X—eXercising the Word of God I Timothy 4:7 and 9 (MSG)
in my life
Yielding to God   Romans 6:13
Zealous for the things of God   I Corinthians 14:12

CPSIA information can be obtained
at www.ICGtesting.com
Printed in the USA
BVHW020053301221
625020BV00003B/77